The Gruffalo
Summer Nature Trail

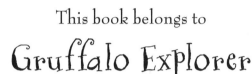

This book belongs to

Gruffalo Explorer

....

Step inside the deep dark wood and join the
Gruffalo for a fun family nature trail.

To be a true Gruffalo Nature Explorer, you'll
need to keep your eyes open and your ears to the ground,
and don't forget to take this guide with you!
It's full of games, activities and hundreds of stickers
to keep you looking for and learning about nature.
So run outside while the weather is warm
and see how much nature you can spot!

If it's sunny outside,
don't forget the sun block

And maybe even a hat!

Take a stroll through the deep dark wood . . .

You'll need your sticker page for this activity

Grass

Feather

Pine cone

Sticks

Tree bark

Tree stump

Green leaf

Crunchy leaves

Bird

EXPERT EXPLORERS

Nest

Blue flower

Beetle

Look at all the pictures below. How many of
these can you see on your stroll?
Put a Gruffalo paw sticker next to each one.

Snail

Moss

Butterfly

Ants

Spider's web

Squelchy mud

Squirrel

Yellow flower

Worm

~ Did you find them all? Come back another day if not!

Mushrooms

Caterpillar

Hollow tree

Colours in Nature

For every colourful thing you see, find the matching colour sticker and stick it in the matching colour box.

What can you see that's green?

Leaf

We've done the first one for you

~ I can see a green wart!

Bugs often use their colour as camouflage, which means we blend in with our background

You can write down what you've seen, or draw a picture.
Then try counting up the stickers at the end of your walk.

What can you see that's brown?

I think I saw a small, brown mouse!

Blending in helps us hide from creatures
that might want us for lunch!

Colours in Nature

What can you see that's red?

~ I see a red, bushy tail

What can you see that's blue?

~ I see a blue flower

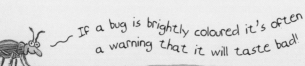

~ If a bug is brightly coloured it's often a warning that it will taste bad!

What can you see that's yellow?

~ I see some yellow eyes!

~ Male birds are often more brightly coloured than females because they like to show off

What can you see that's black?

~ I can see a black tongue!

Name That Tree

There are many different types of tree, each with differently shaped leaves. How many can you see? Put a special leaf sticker next to each one you spot.

Hawthorn	Birch	Alder	Oak
Ash	Hazel	Holly	Maple
Elder	Horse Chestnut	Sycamore	Beech

How many fallen leaves can you collect on your walk?
Try and collect as many different types as you can.
Can you find any that match the shapes above?

Using the pictures above, can you name the tree they came from?

A Leaf Crown

All good tree spotters deserve a crown!
Here's how to make one:

You will need a paper strip, double-sided sticky tape and some lovely leaves. Make sure your paper strip is big enough to fit your head.

Place one side of the double-sided sticky tape around the outside of the crown, and stick into position.

Use glue or tape to fix the paper into a circular crown shape and double-check that it fits your head.

Once you have all your leaves ready, peel back the top layer of the sticky tape and push the leaves into place.

Impressive!

You could also take the leaves home and make a leaf collage

Mixed-Up Tree

Now you know all about leaves, use your special leaf stickers
to complete each branch of this very unusual tree.
We've done the first one for you.

Ash

Elder

Hazel

Oak

Sycamore

Hawthorn

Birch

Maple

Holly

You can tell how old a tree is from the thickness
of its trunk. The thicker it is the older the tree is!

If you have a favourite leaf you
can stick it in the back of this book

Bugs and Butterflies

In summer you're bound to spot bugs and butterflies. How many of these can you see? Put your special bug spotting sticker by each one.

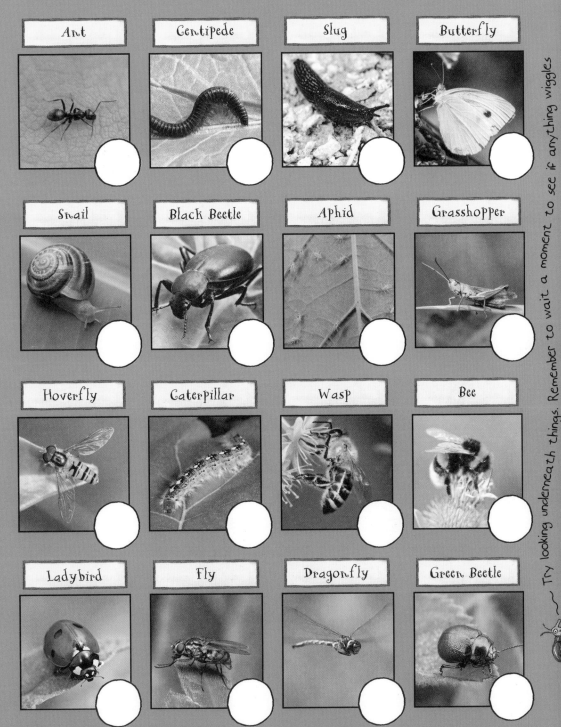

Ant

Centipede

Slug

Butterfly

Snail

Black Beetle

Aphid

Grasshopper

Hoverfly

Caterpillar

Wasp

Bee

Ladybird

Fly

Dragonfly

Green Beetle

Try looking underneath things. Remember to wait a moment to see if anything wiggles

Beautiful Butterflies

How many of these can you see?
Put your special butterfly spotting sticker by each one.

Cabbage White or Large White

Peacock

Gatekeeper

Orange Tip

Small Tortoiseshell

Red Admiral

Did you know that butterflies can see many more colours than we can?

Cosy Nest

If you look carefully you might see a bird's nest up in a tree or in a bush. Did you know that birds don't build nests to sleep in — instead they're a comfy place to lay their eggs and keep their babies warm.

Why not try making your own nest using things found on the forest floor. Sticks, twigs and mud make a strong outside and feathers, grass or wool can make a soft, cosy inside.

If you want to be just like a bird, who only has a beak, try making your nest with just one hand.

If you find leaves and petals on the floor you can make it extra colourful!

High Speed Nature Dash

It's time to use your nature-spotting skills for a quick game.

Build a nest! If you are divided into teams, each will need their own nest.

One person must be the Nature Caller and shout out words from the list below, in no particular order.

Everyone listen to the Nature Caller. The aim is to find something around you that matches what is being called out. Do this as fast as you can and bring it back to the nest.

The fastest person to return to the nest wins a point and the team with the most points wins!

~ I have found a brown rock

Well done! ~

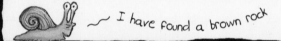

~ Grass can feel tickly

So can dandelion clocks! ~

Nature Caller Word List:
"Can you find something . . ."

Green

Sticky

Brown

Spongy

Tickly

Round

Pretty

Grey

Flat

Shiny

Hollow

Soft

Crunchy

Hard

~ Use the Nature Notes at the back of this book to write about everything you've found

You could even try drawing them! ~

Wonderful Woodland Art

Take a look around you and see what you can use to create some wonderful woodland art. You can leave your picture on the floor for other Gruffalo Nature Explorers to discover!

Seeking Shelter?

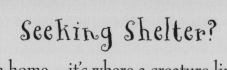

A shelter is a home — it's where a creature lives and sleeps.
They are all around us and some are big, others small.

The Gruffalo's home is quite big! He lives in a cave in the deep dark wood. Can you see any caves?

Fox lives in an underground house. Can you see any holes in the ground that could be Fox's house?

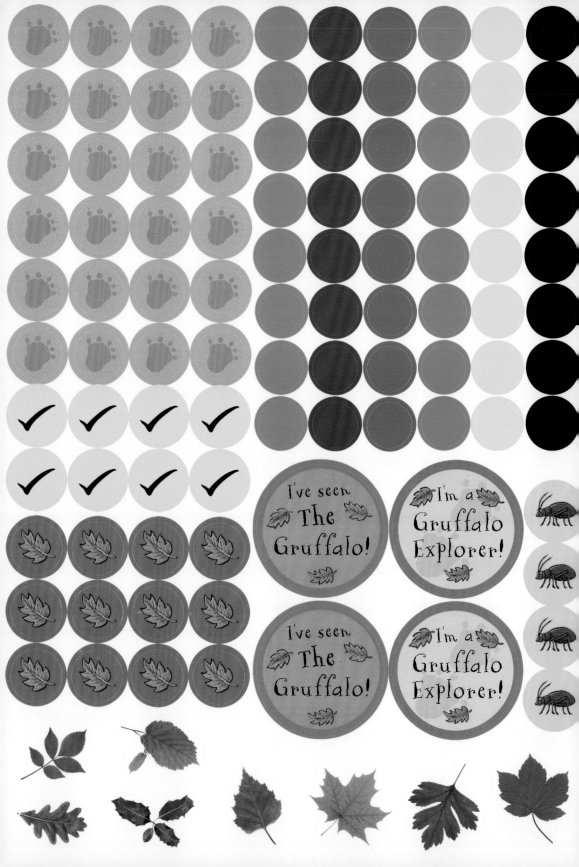

I've seen The Gruffalo!

I'm a Gruffalo Explorer!

I've seen The Gruffalo!

I'm a Gruffalo Explorer!

Happy Habitats

Owl lives in a treetop house.
If you look up at the trees,
can you see Owl's house?

Snake lives in a log pile house.
Can you see a log?
Try turning it over and see
who lives underneath.
Can you see beetles,
worms, or maybe ants?

Ask for help if it's a bit heavy!

And remember to put it back exactly as you found it

If you look very carefully you might
see a small hole in a rock, or a tree.
Maybe Mouse lives there!

Happy Habitats

A habitat is the place where a creature finds its shelter, water, air and food — all the things it needs to survive.

Use your stickers to complete the pictures below.
What might you see near a flower?

What might you find in a tree?

What might you find near or under a log?

What's That Noise?

It's time to stop and listen very carefully. How many of these sounds can you hear on your walk? Put a Gruffalo ear sticker next to each one.

Flies buzzing

Creaky branches

Twigs snapping

Birds calling

Water

Squelchy mud

Rustling leaves

Bees buzzing

Windy trees

Grasshoppers

Birds flapping

Grass swishing

Crunchy stones

Frogs croaking

Footsteps

Falling rain

Try listening carefully with your eyes closed

Sticks and Stones

This is a game for two people.
Firstly, find some sticks and
make a game board
on the floor.

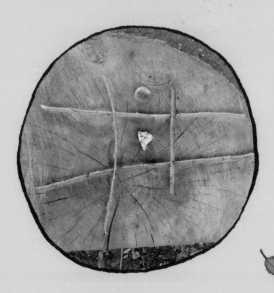

Then collect a pile of stones,
some light, some dark, ready to
play Three in a Row.

Choose either the light or dark
stones and take it in turns to place
your stone on the game board.
The first person to place three
matching stones in a row
is the winner!

You could also use
pine cones for this game

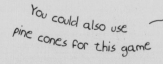

Animal Signs

See if you can spot any signs that creatures have been near. The images below are all clues, so keep your eyes peeled and place a Gruffalo paw sticker next to each one you see.

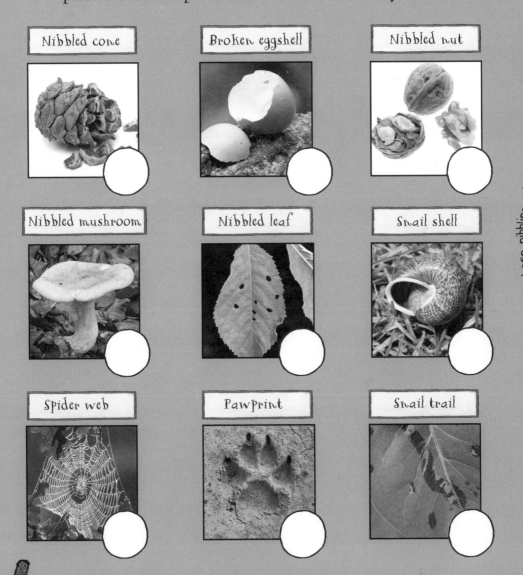

Nibbled cone	Broken eggshell	Nibbled nut
Nibbled mushroom	Nibbled leaf	Snail shell
Spider web	Pawprint	Snail trail

Who's been nibbling the nuts?

A nibbled pine cone could be a sign of a squirrel's lunch, as they can be messy eaters! Holes in leaves are often made by hungry caterpillars, and an empty snail shell is usually a sign that a peckish bird has eaten the snail.

Eyes Down!

The Gruffalo is hard to spot as he's big and brown, just like a tree. But keep your eyes peeled, just in case. If you think you've seen him, reward yourself with a special sticker. It looks like this:

I've seen The Gruffalo!

Gruffalo tracks look like this:

~ But they are very rare . . .

When it rains, the ground becomes muddier, which makes footprints and animal tracks easier to see.

Follow the Trail

If you see one of the prints below, put a tick sticker in the box! ✓

Dog	🐾 🐾	
Bird	🐦 🐦	
Fox	🐾 🐾	
Human	👣 👣	

Why not try making a trail for your friends to follow.
You can use stones or sticks, like this:

Why not place a surprise at the end,
like a flower, shiny stone, or even a nut!

Nature Spotting in the Deep Dark Wood

Look very carefully at the pictures below. Can you find
the missing shapes on your sticker page and put them in the scene?

What have you found?

All of these pictures can also be found in The Gruffalo.
Read the story and see if you can spot them.

Draw a Picture

Your picture could be of you and your family
on the walk, or maybe something you saw, like a
butterfly or a bird's nest in a tree.

Well done, you are now a
Gruffalo Explorer!

Reward yourself with a
special sticker like this

I'm a
Gruffalo
Explorer!

 # Nature Notes

Use these pages to stick in things you find, keep photos of your day or
write poems or stories about the things you have seen.

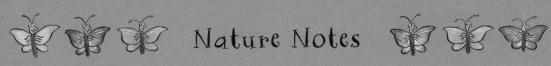

Nature Notes

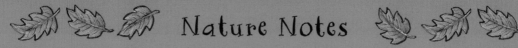
Nature Notes

 # Nature Notes

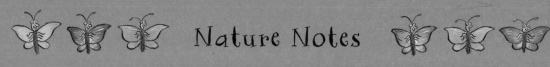